This series of books empowers children to realize that regardless of their age, they can make a difference through kindness and good deeds. The stories will inspire them to rely on God to provide guidance and direction, as they seek to help others.

Today is Rachel's first day at her new school. She and her family recently moved to town to live with her aunt, while her Dad looks for a new job. Rachel is a little nervous, but she is very excited to be at her new school. She hugs her Mom and Dad before she goes inside.

Rachel's Mom reminds her to go to the school office to get her schedule. She tells Rachel that Principal Williams always has someone help new students find their classroom.

Rachel gives her Dad one more big tight hug, and then waves goodbye as she heads to Principal William's office.

When Rachel arrives at the office, Principal Williams greets her and says, "Meet Grace. She is going to show you our school and your classroom." Grace and Rachel sit and talk while Principal Williams gets Rachel's schedule.

Rachel is very happy to meet Grace. She is thankful to have someone help her find her classroom, and is excited to have already met a friend.

Grace looks at Rachel's schedule. She is very excited and says to Rachel, "You're in my class! I will introduce you to all our classmates." They both hurried down the hall to the classroom with big smiles on their faces.

When Grace introduces Rachel, she sees some of the kids whispering and talking. She hears them say, "Why is Grace being nice to her? She doesn't look like us! Or dress like us!"

Grace's best friends are Kristen and Emily. Grace tells them that they should talk to Rachel and make her feel welcome. The girls say, "She is not like us, and we don't want to hang out with her."

At recess, they don't ask Rachel to play kickball with them.

At lunch, the girls don't invite Rachel to sit with them at their table.

Grace sees Rachel sitting alone, looking sad and scared. She feels sorry for her. In her heart, Grace knows she and her friends are not doing the right thing.

On Sunday, Grace, Kristen and Emily meet at church. As they listen to the sermon, they hear the preacher say that we should love others and show kindness to everyone. He read from the Bible: "Do unto others as you would have them do unto you." He explained this meant we should treat people kindly, as we would want to be treated.

He said that God created us all uniquely, and no matter the color of our skin or our differences, we should love each other just as He loves each of us. After hearing the sermon, Grace knew what she was supposed to do.

The next day Grace invited Rachel to eat lunch at the table with her and the other girls. Rachel was grateful, but a little uneasy. She could feel the other girls looking at her, and they were not talking to her.

Grace asked Rachel to tell them more about herself. Rachel says that her family moved here because her Dad lost his job, and that they are living with her aunt. Rachel looks a little sad and tells them shyly, "I don't have a lot of clothes, and most of my clothes are hand-me-downs from my brother. As soon as my Dad starts his new job and saves money, my Mom is going to take me shopping for new clothes. I want to have cute outfits like you have!"

That afternoon, Grace invited Rachel to walk home with her. Kristen and Emily saw them walking together and having fun. Maybe Rachel WASN'T so different, they thought. Maybe they WOULD like hanging out with her.

After Grace walked Rachel to her house, she went to the park to look for the other girls.

When Grace found her friends at the park, she told the girls she wanted to talk to them. She reminded them of the message that they had heard in church. "Remember", Grace said, "we are supposed to treat others as we would want to be treated. We are hurting Rachel's feelings when we leave her out and treat her differently. God created us all uniquely, but he loves us all equally. We should do the same and accept people and show them love. The color of our skin or the way we look should not matter. Rachel is a nice person and wants us to accept her. I like her a lot!"

All of a sudden, Kristen said, "I know what we can do! We all have a lot of clothes, and we don't wear all of them. What if we give some of our clothes to Rachel?" Emily said, "We should do that!" They decided to bring the clothes to Kristen's house and then invite Rachel over.

The girls went home and gathered their extra clothes and brought them to Kristen's house. Then they invited Rachel to come over. They couldn't wait for her to get there and see the surprise they had for her. They felt so good about what they were doing to help her!

Kristen's dog, Rylie, was right in the middle of it all.
Kristen said, "Look! Even Rylie has clothes to show Rachel!"
The girls laughed so hard!!

When Rachel walked in, she seemed confused to see all the clothes out. The girls told her that these were extra clothes they had, and they wanted her to have them. Rachel could not believe what she was hearing and seeing.

She asked, "All of these beautiful clothes are for me?"

"Yes!", said the girls.

They told her that they had more than they needed and wanted to share with her. That made Rachel have the biggest smile they had ever seen!

She began holding up the clothes and looking in the mirror. She had so much fun trying on the outfits and selecting the ones she wanted.

Rachel couldn't believe what a kind thing they were doing for her by giving her these gifts. She chose the outfits she wanted, and then hugged them so tight and thanked them for sharing with her.

The next day, Rachel came to school in one of her new outfits! She felt so happy, and so grateful for her new friends!

That day at recess, the girls were talking. Grace said, "I have a great idea. Let's have a slumber party at my house tonight!" Everyone agreed, and they started planning. She asked Rachel, "Can you come to the party?"

Of course Rachel was thrilled and immediately said "Yes, I can't wait!" She hurried home to ask her Mom and pack her bag.

That night they all went to Grace's house. Her Mom had made yummy snacks for them, and Grace's Dad grilled so much delicious food. They ate on the patio and listened to music. Grace thought her idea had turned out perfectly and was thrilled that Rachel was having so much fun with them.

After they finished eating, the girls went to Grace's room to hang out. They listened to music, painted their toenails, and played games.

As they were talking, Rachel thanked them for all they had done for her. She told them how she had felt so scared her first day of school. She knew she might not fit in because sometimes people judged her based on the color of her skin or how she dressed.

The girls felt really bad about how they had behaved. They apologized to Rachel and told her that they had not realized how she was feeling. Now they understood that not accepting her just because of the way she looked was wrong and hurtful. They promised to never act that way again - they would show kindness to all, remembering to treat people as they would like to be treated.

Rachel explained to them that she was thankful for the clothes they had given her, but she was even more thankful that they accepted her just as she was. They gave her friendship and love, which made her feel so special!

She knew they had done what God wanted them to do, and promised she was going to do the same. Rachel said "My wish is to make someone feel as special as you have made me feel! And that is just what I am going to do!"

You can do the same and make a difference in someone else's life! Show kindness and love whenever you can. Treat everyone equally, even if they may not look the same as you on the outside. Remember, God created each of us and loves us all equally. Doing good deeds for others will not only make them happy, but it will also make you feel good and will bring you joy and blessings. If we each accept people and reach out to help them, what a positive difference we can make in our world!

Do unto others as you would have them do unto you.

Matthew 7:12

GOOD DEEDS FILL NEEDS

Made in the USA
Middletown, DE
28 November 2020